GRAPHIC POETRY

Mother to Son
Harlem Night Song

Langston Hughes

Series Editor • Glen Downey
Art • Martin Wittfooth

In creating the graphic poetry in this collection, we made many choices interpreting the poet's original language and ideas. Our hope is that these graphic poems will get you to see poetry — literally and figuratively — in a whole new way!

SCHOLASTIC

175 Hillmount Road
Markham, Ontario
L6C 1Z7

A Rubicon book published in association with Scholastic Canada

Rubicon © 2009 Rubicon Publishing Inc.

Editorial Director: Amy Land
Project Manager/Editor: Christine Boocock
Creative Director: Jennifer Drew
Art Director: Rebecca Buchanan
Graphic Designer: Jason Mitchell

The publisher gratefully acknowledges the following for permission to reprint copyrighted material in this book.

Every reasonable effort has been made to trace the owners of copyrighted material and to make due acknowledgement. Any errors or omissions drawn to our attention will be gladly rectified in future editions.

"Mother to Son," "Harlem Night Song" from THE COLLECTED POEMS OF LANGSTON HUGHES by Langston Hughes, edited by Arnold Rampersad with David Roessel, Associate Editor, copyright © 1994 by The Estate of Langston Hughes. Used by permission of Alfred A. Knopf, a division of Random House, Inc.

INTRODUCTION

Mother to Son perfectly illustrates one of the most important qualities of Langston Hughes' poetry: authenticity. This is a term that refers to how truthful or real we feel a work of literature to be. This poem is a dramatic monologue in which a woman talks to her son about the challenges she's faced in her life, while encouraging him never to give up. The speaker has seen and experienced many things. Her words teach us that the challenges of life lie not in the obstacles we confront, but in our courage to overcome them.

In the graphic poem, artist Martin Wittfooth uses powerful images to bring Hughes' dramatic words to life.

It's had tacks in it,

And splinters,

And boards torn up,
And places with no carpet on the floor—
Bare.

And turnin' corners,

And sometimes goin' in the dark
Where there ain't been no light.

THE POEM

Mother to Son

Langston Hughes

Well, son, I'll tell you:
Life for me ain't been no crystal stair.
It's had tacks in it,
And splinters,
5 And boards torn up,
And places with no carpet on the floor —
Bare.
But all the time
I'se been a-climbin' on,
10 And reachin' landin's,
And turnin' corners,
And sometimes goin' in the dark
Where there ain't been no light.
So boy, don't you turn back.
15 Don't you set down on the steps
'Cause you finds it's kinder hard.
Don't you fall now —
For I'se still goin', honey,
I'se still climbin',
20 And life for me ain't been no crystal stair.

Harlem Night Song

Harlem Night Song

sings the praises of Harlem, a neighbourhood in New York City that has long been a centre of cultural importance for African Americans. In some of his poems, Langston Hughes talked about the problems and social issues that he saw confronting the residents of Harlem in his day.

However, in many of his works, Hughes also captured the beauty of Harlem and its African-American community. This is what he did in "Harlem Night Song." As we read the poem, we know that for Hughes, Harlem was not simply a place of struggle, social unrest, or hardship, but one of beauty, life, vibrancy, song, and poetry.

Across
The Harlem roof-tops

Moon is shining.
Night sky is blue.

Stars are great drops
Of golden dew.

Down the street

A band is playing

Singing.

HARLEM NIGHT SONG

Langston Hughes

Come, Let us roam the night together
Singing.

I love you.

Across
5 The Harlem roof-tops
Moon is shining.
Night sky is blue.
Stars are great drops
Of golden dew.

10 Down the street
A band is playing

I love you.

Come,
Let us roam the night together
15 Singing.

BETWEEN THE LINES

MOTHER TO SON

Langston Hughes is a master of **diction** (choice of words) and **tone** (manner of expression). "Mother to Son" is written in free verse. This gives the poem a natural, conversational feel. Hughes also makes the mother sound authentic by having her speak matter-of-factly and in dialect. Hughes understands how characters relate to one another and he chooses language they would use in real life.

> Well, son, I'll tell you:
> Life for me ain't been no crystal stair.

Then in lines 14 and 15 of the poem, the mother's tone changes. Looking back at the struggles she has faced reminds her how important it is for her son to stay strong and to not "set down on the steps."

The mother uses symbolism and metaphor to get through to her son. The "crystal stair" is a symbol of the wealth and glamour she has lived without. A metaphor is a comparison without using the words "like" or "as." Here, life is a splintery, dark, worn staircase that the mother has struggled her whole life to climb. Her words are meant to encourage, warn, and most of all talk some sense into her disillusioned son.

dialect: *language or vocabulary characteristic of a specific group of people*

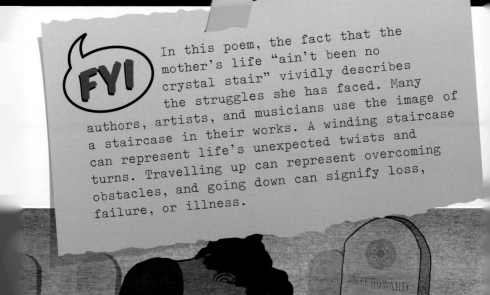

- Read through the graphic poem silently. Use the illustrations to help you understand the mood of the speaker. Practise reading the poem aloud, changing your tone to fit the words. When you are ready, present a dramatic reading of the poem to a small group. Ask your listeners to tell you what they think of your reading.

- Write a poem, entitled "Son to Mother," in which the son responds to his mother's advice. Think about how the language and tone of your poem might be similar to or different from that of Hughes'.

HARLEM NIGHT SONG

In this poem, the speaker is in love, whether it is with an actual person, with the sights and sounds of the music-filled moonlit evening, with Harlem itself, or with all of these things. The poem's relaxed **tone** reflects the speaker's contentment with the world around him. The speaker's use of language conveys a sense of comfort and ease which suggests that he wants nothing more than to soak up the experience of a Harlem night:

> Come, Let us roam the night together
> Singing.
>
> I love you.

During his career, Hughes was heavily influenced by jazz music. In his poetry, he often copied the rhythms, moods, and free forms of jazz. When describing jazz poetry, literary critic Harold Bloom wrote that it "moves with the bouncy rhythms and exuberance that characterize the music. The sentences are casual and short-winded; the phrases are short, tumbling after one another in rapid succession." "Harlem Night Song" reads like a free verse poem. Its combination of forms and styles remind the reader of jazz.

Hughes once said that he "tried to write poems like the songs they sang on Seventh Street." And jazz and blues didn't just influence his poems! Though best-known for his poetry, Hughes also wrote musicals, operas, and choral compositions.

- Which of the illustrated panels do you feel best captures the tone of Hughes' poem? Be sure to use evidence to support your choice.

- Write a short poem about a place that is special to you, or an event that you truly enjoyed. Let the rhythm, diction, and tone express your feelings.

Most of my own poems are racial in theme and treatment, derived from the life I know. In many of them I try to grasp and hold some of the meanings and rhythms of jazz.

— Langston Hughes

Langston Hughes (1902–1967) was an African-American writer and one of the most influential figures of the Harlem Renaissance. This was a period between the end of World War I and the early 1930s when African-American writers, artists, and intellectuals promoted the idea of celebrating Black history, culture, and pride.

Langston Hughes

Hughes had a difficult childhood, which included the separation of his parents. However, this period of his life had a strong influence in shaping his career as a writer. Raised largely by his grandmother, Hughes grew up listening to the stories she told him, stories that gave him a love of the oral traditions of his people.

Hughes' first book of poetry, *The Weary Blues*, was published in 1926. Apart from poetry, Hughes also wrote novels, short stories, and plays. Hughes' works continue to be influential and important because of their focus on the African-American experience. "He wanted to tell the stories of his people in ways that reflected their actual culture, including both their suffering and their love of music, laughter, and language itself," according to the Academy of American Poets. The two poems in this book, "Mother to Son" and "Harlem Night Song," are perfect examples of this.

Langston Hughes rehearses one of his plays in 1942

INDEX

Photo Credits